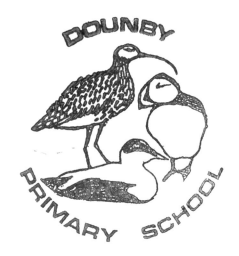

# WHAT WE CAN DO ABOUT

# CONSERVING ENERGY

## Donna Bailey

# WHAT WE CAN DO ABOUT

# CONSERVING ENERGY

## Donna Bailey

**Franklin Watts**

London   New York   Sydney   Toronto

Original text © 1991 Donna Bailey
© 1991 Zoe Books Limited

Devised and produced by
Zoe Books Limited
15 Worthy Lane
Winchester
Hampshire SO23 7AB
England


First published in 1991
in Great Britain by
Franklin Watts Ltd
96 Leonard Street
London EC2A 4RH

First published in Australia by
Franklin Watts Australia
14 Mars Road
Lane Cove
New South Wales 2066

ISBN 0 7496 0530 8

A CIP catalogue record for this book is available from the British Library.

Printed in Italy

Design: Julian Holland Publishing Ltd
Illustrator: Tony Gibbons
Picture researcher: Alison Renwick

**Photograph acknowledgements**
$t$ = top $b$ = bottom
Cover: J Allan Cash Photo Library.
p6$t$ Chris Fairclough Colour Library, 6$b$, 8 Hans Reinhard/Bruce Coleman, 9 Jimmy
Holmes/The Environmental Picture Library, 9$b$ J Allan Cash Photo Library, 10
Chris Fairclough Colour Library, 12$t$ Robert Harding Picture Library, 14 Courtesy
of Mr & Mrs R Holmes/Fine Art Photo Library, 15$t$ Chris Fairclough Colour
Library, 15$b$ S & R Greenhill, 16$t$ Department of Energy, 16$b$ Chris Fairclough
Colour Library, 17$t$ Sue Boulton/ICCE, 17$b$ Chris Fairclough Colour Library, 18
Chris Fairclough Colour Library, 20$t$ S & R Greenhill, 20$b$ Mike Jackson/The
Environmental Picture Library, 21 Tony Morrison/South American Pictures, 23
Alex Bartel/Science Photo Library, 24 Chris Fairclough Colour Library, 25$t$ Paul
Glendell/The Environmental Picture Library, 25$b$ Intermediate Technology, 26
Chris Fairclough Colour Library, 27 Geoff Renner/Robert Harding Picture Library.

# Contents

# Forms of energy

There are several different kinds of energy. In order to move, run around and play you need chemical energy which you get from food. An electric cooker uses electrical energy and changes it to heat energy. If someone throws a ball through the air and you jump to catch it, both you and the ball have movement energy. Different kinds of energy can be changed from one form into another, but the total amount of energy in the world stays the same.

Earth's energy comes from the Sun, most of it as heat and light. Plants are able to use the Sun's energy to make new plant material so that they can grow. Animals use the chemical energy stored in the plant food to help them grow and to move. Many animals, including people, need energy in the form of heat to keep warm.

Our bodies use energy all the time, even when we are asleep. We use energy to breathe, to laugh, to work and to play. A boy of 11 might use the same amount of energy when sitting quietly as a 60 **watt** electric light bulb. Of course he would use much more when walking or running.

We use energy for cooking, to heat or cool our homes, to travel from place to place, and to make machines work. In some countries, people burn plant or animal material, such as wood or dried animal dung, to produce the energy they need for cooking and heating.

In Europe and North America, nearly all the energy we use comes from **fossil fuels** such as coal, oil and natural gas. These fossil fuels come from the remains of plants and animals that lived millions of years ago. Like plants today, these early plants stored the Sun's energy. Heat energy and light energy are released when the fuel is burnt.

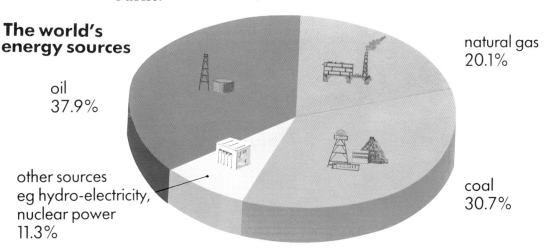

**The world's energy sources**

oil
37.9%

natural gas
20.1%

coal
30.7%

other sources
eg hydro-electricity,
nuclear power
11.3%

There are only limited amounts of fossil fuels in the Earth, and we are using them up very quickly. Scientists think that if we continue to use fuels at the present rate, supplies of oil will run out by the year 2025. Natural gas will not last much longer and coal will only last for about 300 years.

When fossil fuels are burnt to provide energy, they produce other substances that harm, or pollute our surroundings. For example, some **power stations** burn coal to make electricity. The gases given off from the power station join with water vapour in the air. This later falls as **acid rain**, which kills trees – as has happened in the picture.

If wood is used as a fuel, new trees can be grown to replace those cut down. However, if no new trees are planted, or if the wood is used too quickly, people have to travel further from their homes to find fuel. This takes more time and effort and may also leave large areas of ground bare of tree cover. Tree roots and branches help to hold the soil together. Bare areas may have all their top soil washed away by the rain. These soil-less areas cannot be used for growing crops and trees.

# Energy in our homes

We use energy in winter to heat our homes, while in summer, **air conditioning** or fans keep buildings cool.

We also use energy to cook our meals, to light our homes and to heat water for our baths and showers. Machines, such as vacuum cleaners, televisions, washing machines and refrigerators all use energy. In Europe and North America between 30 and 45 per cent of all the energy produced is used in homes, and so it is important that we conserve as much energy as possible.

A lot of the energy we use to warm our homes is wasted, because the heat goes where it is not needed. Insulation is needed to stop houses losing heat to the outside, or to keep houses cool in hot weather. A cavity wall with air in the gap between two surfaces helps provide some insulation. Still air does not carry heat very well, so it is more difficult for heat to cross the gap and escape.

When fuels seemed cheap and plentiful, people did not worry about insulation. But since the 1970s, we have begun to understand the need to use less fuel and save energy, and insulation has become an important part of building work.

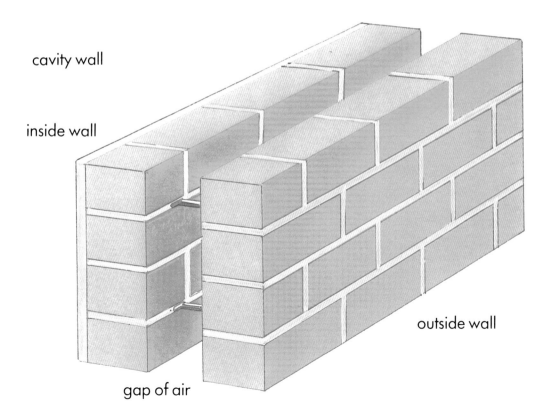

cavity wall

inside wall

outside wall

gap of air

# Keeping the heat in

Many people add extra insulation to their homes to conserve energy. Our picture shows a house-owner putting a thick layer of insulating material in his loft to stop heat escaping through the roof. Find out how well your house is insulated. Ask your parents if your home has **double glazed** windows, loft insulation or **cavity wall insulation.** All these methods of insulation help to cut down heating bills as well as helping to conserve energy.

## Double glazing

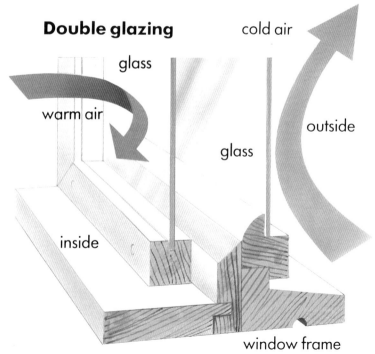

cold air

glass

warm air

outside

glass

inside

window frame

Extra insulation can be added to windows fairly easily by taping clear polythene to the window frames. Air is trapped between the window and the polythene, making a form of double glazing. Curtains drawn across the windows also trap air behind them, so it makes sense to draw curtains as soon as it gets dark. Fitted, wall-to-wall carpets with a thick layer of underfelt, or even newspapers, provide good insulation over bare floors.

Badly fitting doors and windows not only cause cold draughts, but also add to the heat lost from homes. Before the beginning of each winter, you could help your parents to check that the doors and windows fit tightly. Hold a feather by the edge of a door or window and see whether it is blown by any draughts, or use your hand to feel whether any cold air is coming in. **Draught excluders** help stop any draughts you find and can be bought from hardware shops.

In a poorly insulated house heat from inside escapes and energy is wasted. The diagram shows the amount of heat lost through uninsulated lofts, walls, doors, windows and floors.

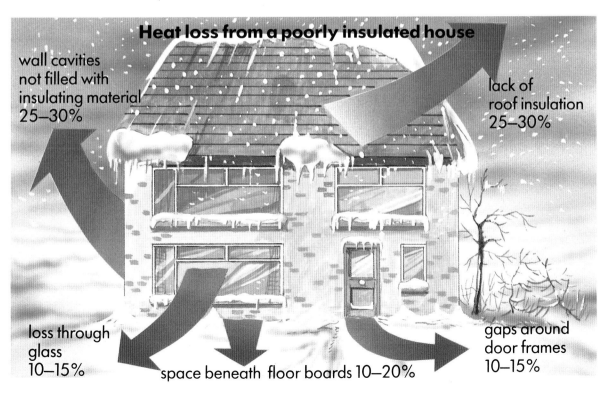

**Heat loss from a poorly insulated house**

wall cavities not filled with insulating material 25–30%

lack of roof insulation 25–30%

loss through glass 10–15%

space beneath floor boards 10–20%

gaps around door frames 10–15%

# Using less heat

In the past, people in cold countries had only wood or coal fires to keep their houses warm. It was difficult to keep warm, so people wore thick clothes. Today, it is easier to keep warm because many houses have **central heating** and more efficient fires. However, by putting on extra clothes, and turning down the central heating or fire, people could easily use less energy.

Most central heating systems have a central **thermostat** which controls the temperature at which the heating is turned on and off. Suggest

to your parents that they try turning
down the thermostat by one degree.
You would probably all still be warm
enough but would be using less heat
energy.

Some heating systems have
individual thermostats on each
radiator. These can be used to set
different temperatures in different
rooms. A radiator can be turned
off when the room is not being used.
But doors between rooms at
different temperatures should be
kept shut.

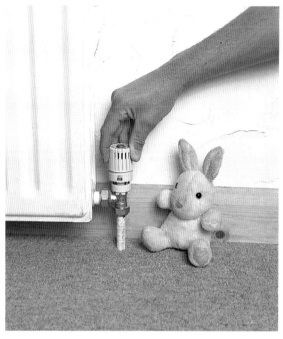

We use energy for heating water as
well as for heating rooms. Your
family may be able to save energy by
turning down the thermostat on the
water heater. Water at a temperature
of 60°C (140°F) is quite hot enough
for most people. You can also save
energy by not wasting hot water.
Always put the plug in the sink when
you wash your hands or do the
washing up, so that hot water is not
wasted. Also make sure that you turn
off hot water taps properly.
A dripping tap could waste enough
water in a day to fill a bath.

# Using less light

If you look at the writing on a light bulb you may see "60W" or "100W". "W" stands for watt. You can save energy by using a 60 watt bulb instead of a 100 watt bulb in places where less light is needed. In the picture, the lamp on the right has a 100 watt bulb and the lamp on the left has a 60 watt bulb.

Also remember to switch off lights when they are not needed.

SWITCH OFF UNWANTED LIGHTS

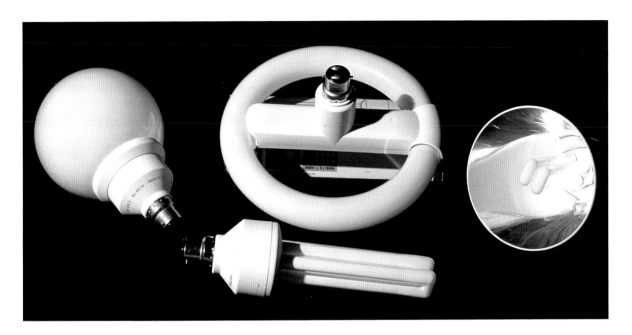

You could also encourage your parents to fit **energy efficient** bulbs. Most ordinary light bulbs produce a lot of heat as well as light. Energy efficient bulbs stay cooler and therefore use less electrical energy, but still provide the same amount of light. They are more expensive to buy, but energy efficient bulbs, like those in our picture, last about eight times longer than ordinary light bulbs.

**Fluorescent lights** also use less electricity and last longer than ordinary bulbs. However, they use most electricity when they light up, so they should not be switched on and off too frequently.

# Saving energy in the home

Most of the machines we use in our homes, like washing machines, cookers and refrigerators, need energy. There are some simple ways in which we can save energy when we use these machines. Always make sure you open the fridge or freezer door for as short a time as possible, and make sure you shut the door properly afterwards. Whenever possible wait until there is a full load before using the washing machine, or use a half-load setting if only a few clothes need washing.

## Ways of using less energy

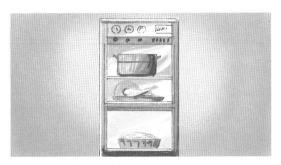

an oven should be used to cook several dishes at once

vegetables should be cut into small pieces to save energy and time

a small pan should be used to cook small amounts of food

a pressure cooker cooks food more quickly than an open saucepan

Encourage your family to think about saving energy when they are cooking. Microwave ovens use 20 per cent less energy than normal electric ovens. Slow cookers use only as much energy as a 100 watt light bulb, and the slow cooking also improves the taste of the food. Other ways of using less energy when cooking are shown in the diagram.

# Energy for transport

People all over the world use a huge amount of energy to travel from place to place. We could all save energy if we travelled more often by train or by bus. Trains and buses are more energy efficient than cars because they use less fuel for each person carried.

Bicycles use no fossil fuels, and for a short journey or a family outing, it is often quicker and more fun to use a bike than to go by car.

If your parents have to replace their car, ask them to consider buying a model which is more energy efficient. Many European manufacturers are now designing cars that can do over 28 km per litre (80 mi per gal). Also a journey done at a steady speed of about 80 km (50 mi) per hour will use less petrol than the same journey done at 112 km (70 mi) per hour.

In some countries, such as Brazil and Zimbabwe, other fuels, apart from petrol, are used to run cars. Fuel alcohol and ethanol are made from plant waste. Plant waste is a **renewable** resource which will not run out. Using these types of fuels helps to conserve energy tied up in **non-renewable** fossil fuels.

# Electrical energy

Much of the energy we use in our homes and factories is in the form of electrical energy. Most electrical energy is made by burning fossil fuels, although some comes from **nuclear power** and **water-driven power.** A small amount of electrical energy is also made from movement energy in the wind and tides.

When electricity is made in a power station, the coal, oil or gas is burnt and the stored chemical energy is changed into heat energy. This heat changes the water in the boilers to steam. The steam turns the blades of turbines which drive the generators that make electricity.

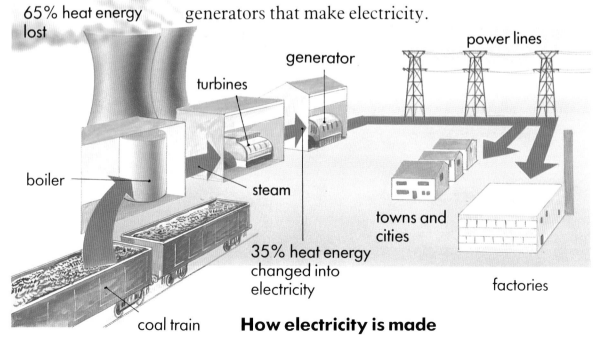

65% heat energy lost

power lines

generator

turbines

boiler

steam

35% heat energy changed into electricity

towns and cities

factories

coal train

**How electricity is made**

Burning coal in a power station is a very inefficient way of using energy because only about 35 per cent of the energy stored in the coal goes into producing the electricity. The rest changes into heat energy and is lost into the air through the cooling towers of the power station, or lost in the water used to cool the remaining steam.

It is possible to make use of some of the waste heat from electricity generation. In Denmark about 33 per cent of homes are kept warm in winter using waste hot water from nearby power stations.

Our picture shows electricity cables, supported by pylons. Even more energy is lost during the processes which make electricity safe so that it can come into our homes, factories and schools.

# Energy conservation worldwide

Because all forms of energy seem to be so readily available, we use far more than is necessary. Some of us use more than others. On average, each person in Europe uses 15 times as much energy as each person in Africa or Asia. The average American uses 30 times as much as an African or Asian person.

Since the mid-1970s, people have begun to realize the importance of conserving energy. Some countries now have programmes to encourage people to save energy. Electrical companies offer energy **audits** or surveys, where an expert visits people's homes and suggests ways in which the family can conserve energy.

In countries where the winters are very cold, people build super-insulated houses. These houses have lots of insulation to keep the heat in and save energy. The new house in our picture has extra thick insulation between the walls and in the roof. More than half the new houses in Saskatchewan, Canada, are now super-insulated. They do not need any heating at all inside, even when the temperature outside falls well below freezing.

Energy conservation in places such as Europe and North America is important because people in these areas use most of the world's energy. In some other countries, energy conservation is important for different reasons. When wood is scarce and you have to walk long distances to collect supplies, it makes sense to conserve the supplies you have. One way in which energy can be saved is to burn wood in more efficient cooking stoves. Tests show that more efficient stoves use only about 30 per cent of the wood used on an open fire.

# Activities

1  Make a list of some of the ways you could save energy at home or at school. Design a poster showing one or more of these ways.

2  Do a survey and find out how people travel to your school. On a piece of paper, record in columns how many walk, how many cycle, how many come by bus, how many come by car with their parents, and how many get lifts with other people and their children. Then mark on a map the area where each person lives. How many people could save energy by changing the way they come to school?

3 Find out as much as you can about the alternative energies to fossil fuels, such as wind energy, solar powered energy and energy from waves and tides.

Write to the electricity companies and Ministry of Power to find out what they are doing about alternative energy.

4 Look at the electricity meter in your home. Take a reading at the same time every day for a week and see how many units have been used. You could also take readings during a week of cold weather and compare them with readings taken during a week of hot weather. Is there a difference? Think of some reasons.

**27**

# Glossary

**acid rain:** rain which poisons trees and plants as it falls on them. Acid rain contains poisons from factory and car fumes which are in the air.

**air conditioning:** a method of cooling an enclosed space, like a building, room or car, for comfort in hot weather.

**audit:** a check to test the efficiency of something.

**cavity wall insulation:** insulation, such as foam or polystyrene balls, put into the gap between the inner and outer walls of a house.

**central heating:** a system of warming a whole house from one heating unit.

**double glazing:** a way of insulating windows by leaving a gap between two panes of glass or between a single pane of glass and a sheet of some other clear material.

**draught excluder:** a strip, usually made of metal or plastic, used to stop draughts coming into a house around doors and windows.

**energy efficient:** describes something which wastes as little energy as possible when it does its job.

**fluorescent light:** a bright light made by a special gas-filled tube.

**fossil fuel:** a fuel, such as coal, oil and natural gas, which is found in the ground and consists of the remains of animals and plants that lived millions of years ago.

**insulation:** a way of stopping heat from going where it is not wanted.

**non-renewable:** describes something which cannot be replaced after it has run out.

**nuclear power:** a type of energy produced by the heat made when atoms are split.

**power station:** a building where electricity is made from other fuels.

**renewable:** describes something which can be replaced.

**thermostat:** an instrument which controls temperatures automatically.

**water-driven power:** the force of moving water being used to turn a wheel which drives machinery.

**watt:** a measure of electrical power.

# Index